Floppy saw a rabbit.

1

Floppy chased it.

It went under a fence.

Floppy got wet.

Floppy got muddy.

They took Floppy home.

"What a soggy doggy!"
said Kipper.

They put Floppy in the bath.

Mum and Dad washed him.

Biff and Chip dried Floppy.

Floppy looked clean.

"What a good dog!"
said Kipper.

Oh no!